WELcuM to THE BASH STREET KIDS ANNuaL 2010...

TEECHER duz Not LiKE pRAKTICAL jOKES

TeecH.R du² t LiKE pRAKTICAL jOKES

du
TeecH.

KEEP IT UP!

IN THE HEADMASTER'S STUDY ...

NOW THEN ... 'I' BEFORE 'E' EXCEPT AFTER ...

CRASH!

?!

BOM! BOM!

WHO KICKED THAT BALL THROUGH MY..?

HMM ... NO ONE THERE, SURPRISE, SURPRISE...!

WELL, I'LL FIND OUT WHO DID IT WHEN THEY COME TO COLLECT THEIR BALL ....!

KNOCK! KNOCK!

COME IN.!

KNOCK! KNOCK!

I SAID: COME IN..!

KNOCK! KNOCK!

OH, FOR HEAVEN'S SAKE!

HELLO..?

HMM... I WONDER WHO THAT..?

...WAS...?

AAARGH!

HEH! HEH! THE OLD TRICKS ARE ALWAYS THE BEST!

SICK NOTES

Deer Teechur,

My son danny will be absent from school today cos the SAS are teeching him to climb trees to save starvin orange utans like he is going to do when he gets older. them orange utans have nowwhere to live and that's a shame. We can't take any cos flippin gran and her three yappadoodles are staying with us. Don't give Danny no extra homework cos it is very hard to write things up a tree without fallin down. Yours sinseerly Dannys mum.

Dear Danny's Mum,

Amazing! Your spelling is exactly as bad as Danny's! However, I am so glad to hear that boy is planning a career similar to my own. Indeed, I have worked with a bunch of little apes for many years and one of them is endangered — **THE ONE CALLED DANNY WHO HAD BETTER GET BACK INTO CLASS NOW!**

Yours,

Teacher.

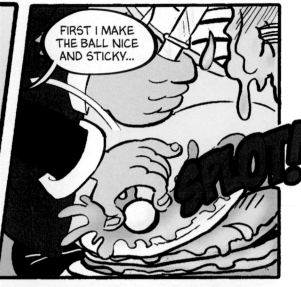

OO! HOPE THAT DOESN'T SPOIL PLUG'S LOOKS!

CRUMP!

TH-THINK I'D BETTER GO IN G-GOAL! TH-THROW ME THE G-GLOVES!

BLEET!

W-WOOPS!

OH, DEAR!

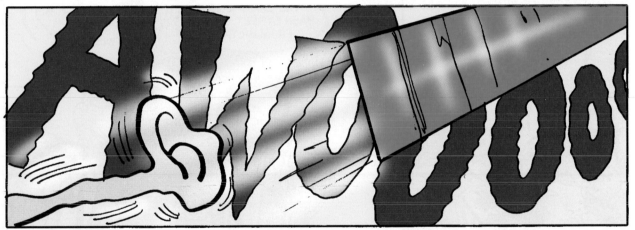

SICK NOTES

Dear Teacher,

I am not letting Smiffy come to school today. We are both sitting watching the BBC news and see that aliens have landed and are blasting our town to bits, eating cars and buses and spreading horrible, people eating, slime everywhere. I don't know what the world is coming to, why only last week that giant blue hedgehog was jumping over all our tall buildings. It is just too dangerous for my poor boy to be out.

Signed, Mrs Smiff.

Dear Mrs Smiff,

I believe you may have a Playstation or X Box attached to your television and are in fact be watching a game. Unplug this and the world will be a much safer place where Smiffy can come to Bash Street School without fear of alien attack. On the other hand, attack from me, whose jacket he accidentally shredded yesterday, is a possibility. Sigh!

Teacher.

EQUALLY NAUGHTY

WHAT A PICTURE

JOBS FOR THE BOY

RIGHT, CLASS... I WANT TO TALK ABOUT YOUR FUTURE...

CAREERS

WHAT DO YOU WANT TO BE WHEN YOU GROW UP?

OLDER!

PFF...!

VERY FUNNY...

THEN MAYBE I SHOULD BE A COMEDIAN!

SPOTTY, YOUR MOUTH IS GOING TO GET YOU INTO TROUBLE!

THEN I'LL GET A JOB IN OUTER SPACE!

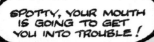

I'LL BE SPACEMAN SPOTTY, FLYING THROUGH THE GALAXY...

RIDDING THE UNIVERSE OF ALIEN WEIRDOS...

TAKE THAT!

出るの*!

* TRANSLATION: AARGH!

HA! HA! HA...! SPOTTY THE ASTRONAUT?

I DON'T THINK SO...!

NOW, CLASS...!

IF SPOTTY WORKS HARD THERE'S NO REASON WHY...

WORKS HARD..?!

IF I HAVE TO WORK HARD, I'M NOT INTERESTED!

SPOTTY, WHAT DO YOU THINK YOU CAN DO IF YOU DON'T LEARN ANYTHING?

BE A TEACHER...

I TOLD YOU THAT YOUR MOUTH WOULD GET YOU INTO TROUBLE...!

I must Not Be Cheeky to Teecher
I must Not Be Cheeky to Teecher
I must Not Be Cheeky to Teecher
I must Not Be Cheeky to Teecher
I must Not Be Cheeky to Teecher
I must Not Be Cheeky to Teecher
I must Not Be Cheeky to Teecher
I must Not Be Cheeky to Teecher
I must Not B

DANNY WOZ HERE

FAT CHANCE!

LOOK, THE SCHOOL'S GOT A CLIMBING FRAME!

WOW!

HEY, LET'S SEE WHO CAN GET ACROSS IT THE FASTEST!

OKAY...! WHO GOES FIRST?

WELL, NOT YOU, YOU FAT LUMP!

WHY NOT ME?

COME ON, FATTY! YOU HAVE PROBLEMS CLIMBING OUT OF BED!

NOW, NOW, SPOTTY! LET'S GIVE HIM A CHANCE...!

THIS'LL BE GOOD FOR A LAUGH!

OKAY, STOP-WATCH AT THE READY...

...AND GO!

OKAY... FIRST UP THE LADDER...

CREAK! I GROAN!

THEN HAND-OVER-HAND ACROSS THE MONKEY BARS...

SQUEAK! GROAN!

...AND DOWN THE SLIDE...! I DID IT!

PUFF! WHEEZE! GASP...!

"LET'S GIVE HIM A CHANCE," YOU SAID...

"THIS'LL BE GOOD FOR A LAUGH!" YOU SAID...

BALL BOY

CAN'T COOK WILL COOK

ALL RIGHT, CHILDREN... TODAY WE'RE HAVING 'CASSEROLE WITH DUMPLINGS.'...!

BETTER KNOWN AS 'DISGUSTING MESS WITH LUMPS'!!

I'D FIND THAT FUNNY IF I DIDN'T HAVE TO EAT IT...

THERE WE GO!

ER... WHY IS THAT DUMPLING GETTING BIGGER?

BLAT!

OH, MY...! I'VE NEVER HAD ONE EXPLODE BEFORE!

YOU HAVEN'T SEEN THE BATHROOM AFTER A MEAL...

I WONDER IF I USED TOO MUCH SELF-RAISING FLOUR?

FLOUR

BLAT! BLAT! BLAT! BLAT! BLAT!

!

APPARENTLY, YES...! AH, WELL, CAN'T BE HELPED...

WHO'S NEXT..?

SICK NOTES

Hi, Teacher, Sur,

It looks like I am not at school this afternoon but that is only cos you can't see me cos I am that skinny cos I have been starved. That shrimp-brain Jamie Oliver told Olive our school cook that I should have 5 portions of fruit or veg every day. DUH! I normally have 23 portions every day! And then my pie and mash! Stupid Geezer! I am now feeling so ill I can only lie on the sofa and wait for the end or the pizza delivery – whatever comes first. If I am still alive I will see you tomorrow. Fatty.

Dear boy,

Sorry to hear you are poorly, could it be something to do with the incident on the football field this morning when you ate the football because it reminded you of a dumpling? Best take some exercise and trot round to the school immediately. If you do not then trouble is on the menu for you!!! Teacher.

STREWTH - IT'S THE TRUTH!

ON THE RUN

ONE DAY, DURING P.E...

I HATE CROSS-COUNTRY RUNNING ...!

ME TOO!

ME TOO!

YEAH..! I HATE CROSS-COUNTRY RUNNING AS WELL!

PAH..! ISN'T THAT JUST LIKE A GIRL ?!

ALWAYS MOANING ...!

THEY'RE JUST NOT AS STRONG AS BOYS!

NOT AS STRONG AS BOYS, HUH ?

BARGE!

ALWAYS MOANING ?

EEK!

JUST LIKE A GIRL, HM?

SPLAT!

WELL, WHAT HAVE YOU GOT TO SAY NOW ?

BIT MUDDY, THAT RUN!

YEAH!

ESPECIALLY IF YOU'RE A GIRL ...

PUTTING HIS FOOT IN IT

Deer Teechur,

I was absent from school yesterday cos my nose wouldn't stop runnin'. It ran to the bus stop in the morning but didn't get off at the school stop then it ran round to Erberts house but he wasn't in so it ran into the café in the high street and stopped runnin' long enough to eat a doughnut but then ran round to the canal where my brother was fishin' and he gave me a tissue and a fishin' rod and it stopped runnin'. Would you be pleased if I gived you and missus teechur a trout for supper? Love Toots.

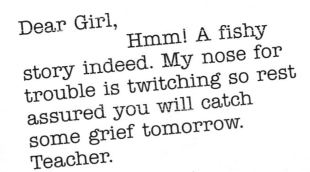

Dear Girl,

Hmm! A fishy story indeed. My nose for trouble is twitching so rest assured you will catch some grief tomorrow. Teacher.

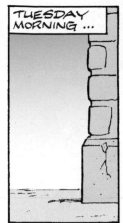
TUESDAY MORNING ...

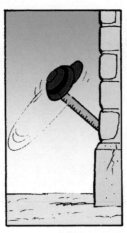
PHEW!

WHAT A ...

SPLAT! SPL SPLAT! SPLAT! SPLAT! SPLAT! SPLAT! SPLA AT! SPLAT

... RELIEF!

WAHEY!

HERE'S MUD IN YOUR PIE!

WEDNESDAY MORNING ...

HI, DENNIS ..! HOW'S IT GOING?

ER ... GRUNT! GRUNT! ... SNORT!

YUP...! KNOW THE FEELING!

DANNY..?

SINCE WHEN DOES DENNIS GO TO OUR SCHOOL?

SPLAT! SPL SPLAT! SPLAT! SPL SPLAT! SPLAT! SPLA SPL AT! SPLAT

WAHEY!

NICE PIE ... I MEAN, NICE TRY, CUTHBERT!

②

BUT, LATER THAT MORNING...

THIS IS DISGRACEFUL!

ABSOLUTELY DISGRACEFUL!

TELL-TALE...!

IF YOU'D LEAVE ME ALONE, I'D HAVE NOTHING TO TELL TALES ABOUT!

THAT'S A GOOD POINT!

SMIFFY, YOU WOULDN'T KNOW A GOOD POINT IF YOU SAT ON ONE!

SILENCE!

I WILL NOT TOLERATE BULLYING IN MY CLASS!

HUH...! WHAT ARE YOU GONNA DO ABOUT IT?

YOU AND YOUR BIG MOUTH, SPOTTY..!

AND I DIDN'T EVEN HAVE A PIE THE FIRST TIME!

SHUT UP, SIDNEY!

TeEcher duZ NoT toleRax BulLee

I DON'T THINK YOU NEED TO WORRY ANY MORE!

BUT, ON THURSDAY MORNING...

SPLAT! SPL SPLAT! SPLAT! SPLAT! SPLAT! SPLA

THAT'S FOR BEING A TELL-TALE!

YEAH..! I 'PIE' WITH MY LITTLE EYE...!

3

⑤

AND SO, ON MONDAY MORNING...

HAS EVERYONE GOT THEIR PIES?

NO!

NOT AGAIN?!

YEAH, AGAIN! HOW COME IT'S ALWAYS ME WHO...

QUIET! HE'S COMING!

HEH! HEH! HEH...!

AH - HAH!

UH-OH...!

SPLAT!

WE'RE COMING, DANNY!

SPLAT! SPLAT! SPLAT! SPLAT!

SPLAT!

SPLAT!

COME ON! LET'S...

GLUMPH!

⑨

WHAT'S COOKING?

ALL RIGHT, CHILDREN, TODAY WE HAVE A CHOICE OF DINNERS...

YOU CAN HAVE FISH AND CHIPS ... OR SALAD...

HMM...! TOUGH CHOICE...!

FISH AND CHIPS FOR ME, PLEASE!

ALL RIGHT!

AARGH..! THAT FISH IS STILL MOVING!

TWITCH! TWITCH!

WHAP!

NOT ANY MORE...!

OH, DEARIE..! AND THE CHIP PAN HAS CAUGHT FIRE!

PTSHSHSHSHSH!

THERE WE GO!

NOW LET'S GET SOME OF THIS FOAM OFF THESE CHIPS!

ER... SORRY, CHILDREN, WHICH OF THE DINNERS DID YOU WANT AGAIN?

SALAD!

SALAD!

SALAD!

SALAD!

SALAD!

SALAD!

SNOTTY BOY

SICK NOTES

Dear Teechur,

As Spotty's skin condishun had got wurse, I took him to the SKIN CLINIC. Unfortunitly there were three leppards, four ladyburds and a dalmashun in front of us in the cue, so it took us till lunch time to get seen. On the way back in the bus, a small boy mistuke my son for a joyn the dots puzzle. He drew a very nice butterfly in felt pen on my sunz left cheek . It tuke me agiz to scrub it all off!

Spotty's Mum

Dear Spotty's Mum,

Isn't it strange how your son's blemishes multiplied just after Art Class. My guess is that stopping Wilfrid flicking his paintbrush might greatly improve Spotty's condition.
I'd recommend a scrubbing brush and some particularly evil smelling soap.

Teacher

ALL AN ACT

IN THE SCHOOL HALL...

TODAY, WE BEGIN A NEW SUBJECT...

ONCE A WEEK, I'LL BE TEACHING YOU ALL DRAMA STUDIES!

ER... WHAT IS DRAMA STUDIES?

DRAMA STUDIES IS ABOUT ACTING AND USING YOUR IMAGINATION!

FOR EXAMPLE, I MIGHT ASK YOU TO PRETEND TO BE BUNNY-RABBITS!

BUNNY-RABBITS?

YES, LIKE THIS..!

BOING!

BOING!

BOING...!

OR YOU MIGHT PRETEND TO BE MONKEYS, LIKE THIS!

OOH! OOH! OOH! OOH!

OOH! OOH! OOH...!

SEE..? JUST LET YOUR IMAGINATION RUN AWAY WITH YOU...!

CAT ATTACK

I THINK IT'S REALLY CUTE THE WAY THAT YOUR CAT SWEEPS THE FLOOR!

IT WOULD BE IF HE DID IT PROPERLY...!

HEY, WINSTON...! MAKE SURE YOU CLEAN OUT THE CORNERS!

WELL, I THINK HE'S SWEET, CARE-TAKER!

HUH!

...YOU WOULDN'T IF YOU KNEW HOW LAZY HE IS...! I MEAN...

MORE TEA, CARE-TAKER?

OOOH... YES, PLEASE!

AND WINSTON... YOU CAN HAVE A SAUCER OF MILK!

AND YOU CAN HAVE MY OLD TEA BAG AS WELL!

PLOP!

HA! HA! HA! LOOK AT HIS FACE!

OH, CARE-TAKER..!

WELL, AT LEAST THAT CAT IS GOOD FOR A LAUGH!

YOU KNOW, SOME-TIMES... WHAT IS IT, WINSTON?

AHAAAGH! SSSRATCH! HIIISSSSS! MEE-OOW!

ER... MAYBE YOU SHOULD CONSIDER GETTING A DOG?!

SICK NOTES

Dear Simple Teacher,

I am not attending your class today because I think your silly lessons are so boring. Your hard maths I could do when I was three and your project on Victorian trousers is pants. I could learn more watching Emmerdale. My clever head hurts when you shout at the other shrimp-brains in the class but you don't seem to care.

Yours sniffingly,
Cuthbert Cringeworthy.

Dear, Dear Boy,

You must not come back to class until you are well again. I can tell by the nasty things you say that my Cuthbykins is upset. I hate having you sit in the same room as the Bash Street Blockheads but the only other room is the janitors store and it has mice!

(I remember the little accident you had when you saw Sidney's pet mouse - though it did have rather a cross look on its face.) Maybe we could bring back your favourite spelling contests. You won every time and oh, how you laughed when Danny spelt pea with two 'e's. Listen to Radio 4 and read some pages from the dictionary and hopefully my star pupil will be well enough to return.

Yours missingly,
Sad Teacher.

SNOW JOKE

HOW ABOUT THIS EXQUISITE ROMAN VASE, FOR EXAMPLE?

PEOPLE WERE PUTTING FLOWERS IN THIS VASE NEARLY TWO THOUSAND YEARS AGO!

COO... HOW EXCITING!

BE STILL, MY BEATING HEART!

SCRATCH! SCRATCH!

ACTUALLY, THERE IS A FUNNY STORY CONNECTED TO THIS EXHIBIT...!

...APPARENTLY, THE WOMAN WHO DISCOVERED THIS VASE FOR FLOWERS... ...WAS CALLED 'ROSE'!

HA! HA! HA! HA!

ANYWAY - MOVING RIGHT ALONG...

...OVER HERE WE HAVE A FINE EXAMPLE OF...

HEY, TOOTS! WHAT DOES THIS NOTICE SAY?

HADRIAN'S WALLPAPER

YAWN...! IT SAYS: DO NOT TOUCH.

WHY NOT?

STRETCH!

...SO WITH THESE BONE KNITTING NEEDLES, THEY COULD MAKE...

MUSEUM GUIDE

CRASH!

HEY, TEACHER! DID YOU HEAR THAT?

NO!... AND NEITHER DID YOU!

MUSEUM GUIDE

2

SMIFFY...YOU DIPSTICK!

D'YOU THINK PEOPLE WILL NOTICE?

QUICK! LET'S TRY AND TIDY UP A BIT!

WHAT'S THAT?

IT LOOKS LIKE A TREASURE MAP!

YEAH...

WHAT DOES ALL THIS MEAN?

NO IDEA - BUT YOU'D BETTER HIDE IT SOMEWHERE BEFORE WE'RE SEEN!

La plaza de Centurio caidus de Londinium

NW-LX SW-C

OKAY.

...AND KEEP IT A SECRET UNTIL WE'RE OUT OF HERE!

THE TOUR FINISHED TEN MINUTES AGO! WHAT HAVE YOU BEEN UP TO?!

SORRY, TEACHER, BUT WHAT I'VE GOT DOWN MY PANTS IS A SECRET!

SMACK!

STOCKS

REALLY?

...WELL, LET'S KEEP IT THAT WAY, SHALL WE?

PSST, DANNY! CAN I HAVE A WORD?

WHISPER! WHISPER! WHISPER!

SOB! SOB! SOB!

ROMAN VASE DO-IT YORE-SELF KITT

WOW! THIS CALLS FOR A GANG MEETING AFTER SCHOOL!

③

AND SO, AFTER TEA-TIME, DANNY HELD A MEETING AT THEIR GANG'S HEAD-QUARTERS (HIS DAD'S GARDEN SHED) ...

SO WHAT'S ALL THIS ABOUT, DANNY?

SEKRIT MEATING IN PROGRIS

BEFORE I TELL YOU, WE MUST ALL PROMISE TO KEEP THIS A SECRET.

THIS AFTERNOON SMIFFY MADE AN AMAZING DISCOVERY.

WHAT – DID HE FIND HIS BRAIN?

NO!

OH ... YOU MEAN IT'S STILL LOST?!

HA! HA! HA! HA! HA! HA! HA! HA! HA! HA! HA!

SOMETIMES, I WONDER WHY I BOTHER..!

SMIFFY, GIVE ME YOUR FOLDER...

THE REASON WE'RE HERE, *EVERYONE*, IS BECAUSE OF THIS TREASURE MAP!

?

SMIFFY! WHAT'S THIS?!

OH, I MADE SOME PHOTOCOPIES AT THE PUBLIC LIBRARY!

YOU *PHOTOCOPIED* A SECRET TREA-SURE MAP?!?

SMIFFY! YOU IDIOT!

BUT I THOUGHT IT WOULD BE NICE IF EVERYONE HAD A COPY.

WHAT, EVERY-ONE IN THE COUNTRY?!

OH, LEAVE HIM ALONE!

AS LONG AS WE COLLECT UP THESE COPIES, THERE'S NO HARM DONE, EH?

HMM...

BY THE WAY, SMIFFY, WHERE'S THE ORIGINAL MAP?

UM...

PUBLIC LIBRARY

HELLO, DENNIS...?

...YOU WILL NOT *BELIEVE* WHAT I JUST FOUND ON THE PHOTOCOPY MACHINE AT THE LIBRARY..!

5

LATER, AT DENNIS'S HOUSE...

SO, ROGER, HOW DO WE USE THIS MAP TO FIND THE TREASURE?

WELL, FIRST WE HAVE TO WORK OUT WHAT THIS STRANGE WRITING MEANS...

HOLD ON! HOW DO WE KNOW THIS MAP'S NOT A FAKE?!?

BASH! BASH! BASH!

IT LOOKS REAL ENOUGH.

WELL, IT WOULD, WOULDN'T IT?!

LOOK, IF I HAD A TREASURE MAP, I'D WANT TO KEEP IT A SECRET...

...ANYBODY WITH A TREASURE MAP WOULD WANT TO KEEP IT A SECRET...

...SO WHO WOULD BE STUPID ENOUGH TO PHOTOCOPY ONE AT THE PUBLIC LIBRARY?!

I CAN THINK OF SOMEONE...

ME TOO...

OH! ...I THINK I KNOW WHO YOU'RE TALKING ABOUT!

D'YOU RECKON THE BASH STREET KIDS ARE LOOKING FOR THE TREASURE?

YES, BUT WE ARE GOING TO FIND IT FIRST!

THIS CALLS FOR LEMONADE AND COOKIES!

OY, MUM! FOOD AND DRINK WANTED UPSTAIRS!

SUCH A POLITE BOY...

...NOT!

6

MEANWHILE, AT THE PUBLIC LIBRARY...

QUIET PLEASE

...AND THERE'S YOUR BOOK OF KNITWEAR PATTERNS.

THANK YOU!

QUIET PLEASE

QUIET PLEASE COME ON - LET'S HAVE SOME HUSH!

BANG!

TRAMPLE! TRAMPLE! TRAMPLE! SCREECH!

PHOTO-COPIES -5p

DRAT!

IT'S GONE!

NOW WHAT DO WE DO?!

SLAM!

YOU GET OUT OF MY LIBRARY, YOU NOISY BUNCH OF HOOLIGANS!!!

NOISY? US?!?

GROWN-UPS ARE SO TOUCHY!

WELL, IT'S GETTING A BIT LATE TO DO ANYTHING NOW...

BUT WE'VE GOT TO MOVE FAST OR SOMEONE ELSE WILL GET THE TREASURE!

LUCKILY, TOMORROW'S SATURDAY.

THUMP!

SPLAT!

OKAY, EVERYONE - GANG MEETING FIRST THING TOMORROW MORNING ...

...RIGHT?

RIGHT!

⑦

HOWEVER, THE BASH STREET KIDS ARE NOT THE ONLY ONES UP FIRST THING SATURDAY MORNING...

I WANNA GET UP!

GODZILLA

I WANNA GET UP! I WANNA GET UP! I WANNA GET UP!

BOING! BOING! BOING!

1 2 3 4 5 6 7 8

I WANNA GET UP! I WANNA GET UP! I WANNA GET UP!

GROAN! I THINK BEA'S AWAKE...

SNORE..!

6.00

...AND ON SATURDAY IT'S YOUR TURN TO GET OUT OF BED!

SNORE..!

HMM... WHERE'S THE VOLUME CONTROL ON THIS THING?

...I WANNA GET UP..!

I WANNA GET UP!

I GET THE HINT!

I THOUGHT YOU MIGHT!

8

⑨

LATER, THAT SAME MORNING...

HI, SMIFFY— I HOPE YOU HAVEN'T DONE ANYTHING DUMB SINCE YESTERDAY?!

DON'T WORRY, DANNY — I'VE BEEN WATCHING HIM LIKE A HAWK!

DANNY'S OVER THERE.

OH!

'ERBERT, WHY DO YOU BOTHER TO WEAR GLASSES?

SPOTTY, PLUG AND FATTY ARE LATE.

OH GREAT...

...WELL, LET'S HOPE THEY KNOW HOW TO KEEP A SECRET!

HEH! HEH! HEH!

HI FANS!

YOU'RE LATE!

THAT'S NO WAY TO TALK TO THE PERSON WHO'S SOLVED THE TREASURE MAP!

NO KIDDING?!

WOW! WHERE'S THE TREASURE?!

AHEM...!

...PLUG!

...FATTY!

...BRING IN THE PRISONER!

10

CUTHBERT?!?

YEAH! IF SWOT-FEATURES HERE CAN'T TRANSLATE THE STRANGE WRITING ON THE MAP, WHO CAN?

HMM...

OKAY, CUTHBERT, WHAT YOU ARE ABOUT TO SEE IS **TOP SECRET!**

IF YOU **EVER** BREATHE A WORD ABOUT THIS TO **ANYONE**...

...THEN YOU WILL NEVER SEE MISTER FLOPSY AGAIN!

WHY CAN'T YOU JUST ASK ME NICELY?

OH, COME ON, CUTHBERT! WHERE'S THE FUN IN THAT?!

HEAR! HEAR!

OH MY WORD! THIS WRITING IS LATIN!

WHAT DOES IT SAY?

IT SAYS: LA PLAZA DE CENTURIO CAIDUS DE LONDINIUM.

WE KNOW **THAT!** WHAT DOES IT **MEAN**?!?

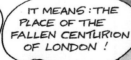

IT MEANS: THE PLACE OF THE FALLEN CENTURION OF LONDON!

THE TREASURE IS IN LONDON?

THE TREASURE IS IN LONDON!

HEH! HEH! HEH! HEH!...

11

LONDON! ...LATER THAT SAME AFTERNOON...

...AND THE TRAIN JUST ARRIVED ON PLATFORM FOUR IS THE TWO-OH-SIX FROM BEANOTOWN...

ARE YOU SURE ABOUT THIS DAY-TRIP, JAMES?

WHY SHOULDN'T I BE?

WELL, ISN'T COMING TO SUCH A BIG PLACE AS LONDON A BIT RISKY?

PAH! WHAT'S LIFE WITHOUT RISK?

LONGER!

SHALL WE GO HOME?

NO WAY! I'M NOT GOING TO LET THIS RUIN MY...

GLURK!

HURRY UP! I DON'T WANT TO LOSE THEM!

YOU WERE SAYING...?

12

OKAY, GANG, IT'S TIME TO LOOK FOR THIS "FALLEN CENTURION" WOSSNAME...

LET'S ALL SPLIT UP INTO PAIRS AND MEET BACK HERE IN TWO HOURS.

HOWEVER, THE KIDS ARE ABOUT TO FIND OUT...

...THAT LONDON IS A **VERY** BIG PLACE...

WE'VE FOUND NOTHING AND MY FEET ARE HURTING!

LET'S ASK A POLICEMAN.

THE FALLEN CENTURION? I'M SORRY, YOUNG MAN, BUT I'VE NEVER...

DOWNING STREET NW 1

10

SPLAT!

FLOUR

SIGH! ...NOT AGAIN!

GOOD SHOT, PRIME MINISTER !!!

HEE! HEE! IT'S GOOD TO BE THE BOSS!

WELL, THIS IS A DEAD-END.

YEAH... I WONDER HOW THE OTHERS ARE GETTING ON.

AT TRAFALGAR SQUARE...

HA! HA! HA! HA!

IT SERVES FATTY RIGHT FOR NEVER SHARING HIS PACKED LUNCH !

GOBBLE! PECK! SNATCH!

13

WELL, HERE WE ALL ARE AND STILL NO SIGN OF THIS "FALLEN CENTURION".

WHAT HAPPENED TO YOU?

DON'T ASK!

WHAT SHALL WE DO, DANNY?

I'M NOT SURE...

THE FALLEN CENTURION PUBLIC HOUSE

...PERHAPS WE SHOULD SPLIT UP FOR ANOTHER TWO HOURS.

BUT THEY'RE STANDING RIGHT IN FRONT OF...

ROGER! QUIET!

I THINK I'LL GIVE THEM A SMALL HINT.

WE NEED A BREAK OF SOME KIND...

CRASH!

WHAT THE..?

HEY! IT'S THE "FALLEN CENTURION"!

WE'VE FOUND IT!

HOORAY!!!

HOORAY?!? WHY, YOU LITTLE GANG OF...

WHAT DID HE CALL US?

I DIDN'T WAIT TO FIND OUT!

OKAY, DANNY, THE TREASURE WILL BE BURIED ONE HUNDRED YARDS AROUND THE NEXT CORNER...

OH, NO!

WOULD YOU BELIEVE IT?!

15

WHO PUT THAT THING THERE?

I SUPPOSE BLOWING IT UP IS OUT OF THE QUESTION?

COME ON! WE HAVE WORK TO DO!

TOOTS, I WANT YOU TO START COUNTING OUT A HUNDRED YARDS.

OKAY, DANNY!

WON'T WE HAVE TO PAY TO GET IN?

ARE YOU JOKING? I'VE GOT A MUCH BETTER IDEA!

AND SO...

ROLL UP! ROLL UP..!

...COME AND SEE THE WORLD'S UGLIEST BOY!

TEST YOUR COURAGE AGAINST HIS FAMOUS FACE-PULLING!

OF ALL THE CHEEK! THEY'RE TRYING TO STEAL MY CUSTOMERS!

TICKETS

16

17

INSIDE THE DOME...

CLANG!

DANNY, I'VE HIT SOMETHING!

SPOTTY, I THINK THIS IS IT!

...THE TREASURE OF THE FALLEN CENTURION!

HERE, DANNY, I'VE GOT A HAIRPIN!

WHAT FOR? YOU HAVEN'T GOT ANY HAIR!

IT'S TO PICK THE LOCK AND OPEN THE BOX, STUPID!

LOOK, SPOTTY, I THINK WE SHOULD GET OUT OF HERE FIRST.

WHY, WHAT'S THE HURRY?

YOU!

YES... ME! DID YOU REALLY THINK YOU COULD OUTWIT DENNIS THE MENACE?!

BLURG!

DOES THAT ANSWER YOUR QUESTION?!

GO, DANNY, GO! WE'LL KEEP DENNIS AND THE REST...

URK!

18

...BUSY...!

BADUMP!

TO HERE
TO THERE

THE WILD WEST EXPERIENCE

NOT OPEN TO THE PUBLIC

THE WILD WEST EXPERIENCE

HEY, MINNIE, WHERE ARE YOU GOING?

DANNY'S IN THERE!

OKAY, SO WHILE HE'S HIDING, LET'S PUT THE OTHERS OUT OF ACTION!

HOW?

I HAVE A PLAN...

MEANWHILE...

HMM... THIS BIT LOOKS LIKE IT HASN'T BEEN FINISHED.

PAINT

EEEK!

HANG ABOUT... IT'S JUST A MODEL!

KNOCK! KNOCK!

I WONDER...

MEANWHILE...

I HOPE YOU LOT LIKE HOSPITAL FOOD!

OH, I'M NOT FUSSY...!

HEY, DENNIS! WE'VE GOT IT!

THEY'VE GOT WHAT?

WHAT D'YOU THINK?!

AFTER THEM!

19

THEY MUST HAVE GOT THE TREASURE OFF DANNY!

LOOK, THEY WENT THROUGH THAT DOOR!

ER, TOOTS...THIS LOOKS SUSPICIOUSLY LIKE A BROOM CUPBOARD!

SLAM! CLUNK!

CLICK!

GOT THEM!

THAT JUST LEAVES DANNY!

...AND HE'S ALL ON HIS OWN! HEH! HEH! HEH!

GREAT! I KNOW EXACTLY HOW TO DEAL WITH HIM!

AND SO...

LIGHTS!

HUH?

CLUNK!

AARGH!

WELL, HOWDY THERE, DANNY-BOY!

DENNIS! WHAT'S GOING ON?!

WHY, YOU AND ME ARE GONNA HAVE US A LITTLE CONTEST!

CONTEST? WHAT KIND OF CONTEST?

IT'S A QUICK DRAW CONTEST. BOTH YOU AND DENNIS HAVE A CATAPULT AND A CREAM BUN...

...AND THE LOSER GETS THE BUN IN THE FACE!

AND THE WINNER?

HAVEN'T YOU GUESSED.?

...THE WINNER GETS THE TREASURE!

MEANWHILE...

THUMP!
...AND A...
THUMP!
...AND A...
THUMP!
...AND A...

CRASH!

HURRY! WE'VE GOT TO FIND DANNY!

BUT ARE THE KIDS TOO LATE ..?

...GO!

...TICK! ...TICK! ...TICK!
...TOCK! ...TOCK! ...TICK
...TOCK! ...T

DIVE!

SNATCH!

ROLL!

GRAB!

REACH!

TUG!

HUH?!

SPLAT!

21

CHING!
CHING!
CHING!

22

AND SO OUR STORY ENDS WITH THE KIDS TAKING A LUXURY CRUISE DOWN THE RIVER THAMES...

CAN I HAVE SOME MORE ICE CREAM?

CERTAINLY! WHICH OF OUR FIFTY-EIGHT FLAVOURS WOULD YOU LIKE?

OH, THIS IS HEAVEN... ...HEAVEN!

DANNY, I HAVE A QUESTION...

...HOW COME DENNIS DIDN'T NOTICE THAT THE BOX WAS EMPTY?

BECAUSE AFTER HIDING THE TREASURE I FILLED THE BOX WITH STONES.

SO DENNIS HAS A TREASURE CHEST FULL OF ROCKS?!

I WISH I COULD SEE HIS FACE WHEN HE FINDS OUT!

YEAH...

...I WONDER HOW HE'LL TAKE IT...

AT DENNIS'S HOUSE—

AAAARGH!

"I HAVE A PLAN", YOU SAID..!

"...GET DANNY ON HIS OWN", YOU SAID!

YEAH! GIVING HIM A CHANCE TO SWITCH THE TREASURE FOR THIS!

CLONK!

AH, WELL ...

...EVEN THE WORLD'S GREATEST MENACE CAN'T WIN THEM ALL!

THE END

CHRISTMAS CRACK UP